Science Digest

SCIENCE & LITERATURE

FOR KIDS

UNIT 23

6 7 8 9   RRD   14 13 12 11 10

Read Well is a registered trademark of Sopris West Educational Services.

ISBN 978-1-60218-559-3
ISBN 1-60218-559-X

Printed in the United States of America
Published and Distributed by

Cambium
LEARNING®
Sopris West®

4093 Specialty Place • Longmont, CO 80504 • (303) 651-2829
www.sopriswest.com

167337/1-10

SCIENCE & LITERATURE
FOR KIDS

Volume 1 | Number 2

The *Read Well Science Digest* is a feature of the *Read Well* reading program, published by Sopris West, a division of Cambium Learning.

Miss Tam's contributions were written by Marilyn Sprick and Ann Watanabe.

4

Letter From the Editor

Dear Readers:

You can imagine how thrilled Minnie Bird, Scraggly Cat, and I were when I was named guest editor for this edition of the *Read Well Science Digest*.

We think the Earth we share is an amazing planet. We didn't know what in the world we wanted to write about. Ghana? Hawaii? Montgomery? We decided to feature the coldest, driest, windiest place on Earth and the wettest places on Earth. We hope you enjoy "Where in the World?"

Yours truly,
Miss Tam, Guest Editor
Retired Librarian and World Traveler

★ freez·ing

When it is so cold that water turns to ice, it is called **freezing**.

We looked outside and saw that the pond had turned to ice, so we knew it was . . .

★ bliz·zard

When it is snowing and the wind is blowing hard, it is called a **blizzard**.

The news report said schools were closed because of the *blizzard.* Describe what the weather was like.

★ e·qua·tor

If you drew a line around the middle of the Earth, that would be the **equator**.

If you stand at the *equator*, it is the same distance to the top of the Earth and the bottom of the Earth. Look at the globe and trace your finger along the equator. What do you know about the equator?

★ = New

6

★ Arc·tic

The **Arctic** is the area at the top of the Earth.

The *Arctic* is a very cold area. If you went on an expedition there, what would you need to bring?

★ Ant·arc·tic

The **Antarctic** is the land at the bottom of the Earth.

The *Antarctic* is another name for the continent of Antarctica. Touch Antarctica.

★ harsh

Something is **harsh** when it is uncomfortable, difficult, or rough!

Antarctica has the *harshest* weather in the world. Do you know what that means?

Now You Try It!

Try defining the next words. Then look up the words in the glossary. Your definition might be better!

★ tem·per·a·ture

Start with "The *temperature* tells us . . ."
Let's find the word on page 86.

u·nique

Start with "Something that is *unique* is . . ."
Let's find the word on page 87.

Where in the World is ...

- the coldest continent?
- the windiest continent?
- the driest continent?
- the coldest, windiest, and driest continent?

Antarctica!

by Susan Blackaby

Answer:
It's the continent
at the bottom
of the world.

Coldest Place on Earth

The coldest place on Earth is the continent of Antarctica. A thick sheet of ice more than 7,000 feet deep covers most of the land. On a winter's day, the temperature can drop to 100 degrees below zero! That is colder than freezing—colder than any of us can imagine. Even in the summer, the temperature is rarely above freezing, so the ice never melts.

What makes Antarctica's temperature unique?

Driest Place on Earth

The driest place on Earth is Antarctica. People think it is a wet place because of the ice, but only about two inches of rain or snow fall each year. It's hard to believe, but the world's largest desert is in Antarctica. It is cold and dry.

What makes Antarctica the driest place on Earth?

Windiest Place on Earth

The windiest place on Earth is also Antarctica. Blizzards sweep across the ice. When the winds blow, the icy blasts make it feel even colder.

Describe Antarctica.
Why would it be difficult to survive in Antarctica?

12

Who Am I?

I am a unique animal. I am the only creature that can live in the coldest, driest, and windiest place on Earth during the harsh winter months. Who am I?

When Antarctica Was Warmer

Antarctica wasn't always so cold, so dry, and so windy. The land has changed over time.

About 500 million years ago, the land that is now Antarctica was closer to the equator. Plants covered its hills and valleys. Dinosaurs roamed from coast to coast.

ANTARCTICA
500 MILLION
YEARS AGO

This is how Earth looked long ago.

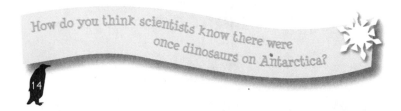

How do you think scientists know there were once dinosaurs on Antarctica?

Slowly, over millions of years, the land drifted south and became colder and colder. Now Antarctica is at the bottom of the world, and it is the coldest place on Earth.

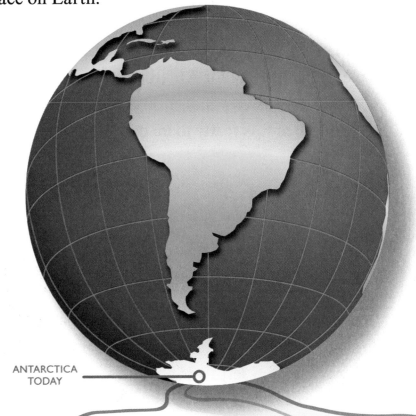

ANTARCTICA TODAY

Who Am I?

Little by little, Antarctica became the frozen place I call home. It went from a jungle to a vast, empty, ice-covered landscape. Now the only other living things that grow in my Antarctic home are tiny animals like worms and small lichens, moss, and algae.

15

Finding Antarctica

About 2,000 years ago, the Greeks thought there must be land at both ends of the Earth—the Arctic and Antarctic. But for thousands of years, no person set foot on Antarctica. About 500 years ago, when explorers finally proved Earth was round, people began looking for Antarctica. Sailing into the icy waters was very dangerous. No one was sure that Antarctica was really there until 1820.

Why did explorers look for Antarctica?

Crossing the Ice

Once people knew where Antarctica was, they wanted to find out more about it. The first explorers came by sea. They left their boats and traveled across the freezing land in sleds. They climbed mountains. They made maps. They collected rocks. (There were fossils in some of the rocks.) The explorers also discovered new wildlife.

Do you think exploring Antarctica was easy or hard? Why?

Who Am I?

Do you want to hear something funny? For many years after Antarctica was discovered, nobody knew anything about me. I was my own little secret. I was discovered in 1902—about 50 years after the first people showed up. Until then, no person had ever seen me!

Now you can see movies about my friends and me! We are famous. Who am I? (For more of the riddle, see pages 18 and 19.)

17

WHAT'S BLACK AND WHITE AND ROYALTY?

by Ann Watanabe

What's black and white
and swims through the sea?

What's black and white
and royalty?

What's black and white
and holds its breath?

What's black and white,
can you guess?

—Nancy Wing
Read Well 2 Field Test Teacher

IT'S AN EMPEROR—AN EMPEROR PENGUIN!

An emperor penguin is a bird. Like all other birds, it has feathers. Unlike most birds, the emperor penguin doesn't fly through the air. Instead, it uses its little wings for swimming. This amazing bird can swim about six miles an hour. An emperor penguin spends most of its time in the sea.

Emperor penguins can swim as deep as 1,800 feet. How deep is that? The deep end of most swimming pools is 10 feet. So 1,800 feet is very deep.

Think about how far an emperor penguin can swim down into the ocean. How would you describe this penguin's swimming abilities?

Quiz

If you were an emperor penguin, how long do you think you could stay underwater?

a) 22 seconds
b) 22 minutes
c) 22 days

Watch for the answer when you reach page 34.

21

WHAT'S WITH THE BLACK AND WHITE TUXEDO?

Emperor penguins look like men dressed up for a fancy party. The penguins aren't dressed up for a party though! The black and white coloring helps protect them. Their black feathers soak up heat from the sun, and their white feathers make it hard for predators to see them in the water.

KEEPING WARM IN THE FREEZING COLD

Emperor penguins need layers and layers of protection to survive the freezing weather.

First layer: The penguins' feathers help keep their body heat inside.

Second layer: Under the tightly packed feathers is a layer of air.

Third layer: Under the skin is a thick layer of fat called blubber.

The layers keep the penguin's body heat in and the cold out.

How do emperor penguins survive the freezing weather?

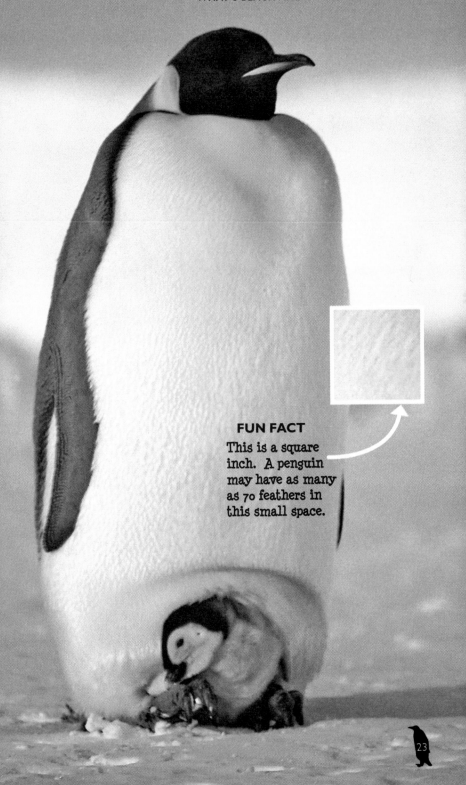

FUN FACT

This is a square inch. A penguin may have as many as 70 feathers in this small space.

23

FROM GENERATION TO GENERATION

Emperor penguins spend most of their lives in the water, but each April, the adults travel across the ice to their nesting ground, called a rookery. Night and day, the animals parade as far as 125 miles to their rookery. There, the females lay a single egg, and the males spend the winter caring for it.

Think of a place 125 miles from your school. Can you imagine walking there? What do the females do at the rookery? What is the responsibility of the males?

NESTING

In their nesting ground, the penguins shuffle on the ice to keep warm. The temperature can drop to an unbelievable 125 degrees below zero. No other animal can survive in this cold—only the emperor penguin. As the temperature falls, the penguins huddle in one big group. They take turns standing in the middle where it is the warmest. This way, they protect the eggs and each other.

What is the rookery? How do the males stay warm? Where do you think the females go?

25

A Penguin's Calendar

by Susan Blackaby

The Antarctic Fall
March, April, May

- After spending their first five years at sea, penguins travel from the sea to the rookery.
- The adult female lays one egg.
- The females return to the sea to eat.

The Antarctic Winter
June, July, August

- The male penguins take care of the eggs.
- When the eggs hatch, the females return with food.
- The males walk back to the sea to eat.

How old are penguins when they begin making their yearly trip to the rookery?

The Antarctic Spring
September, October, November

- Both parents care for the baby penguin.

- The parents take turns going back and forth to the sea for food.

- Babies are fed about once every 16 days.

Look at the pictures and describe what penguins do in the fall, winter, spring, and summer.

The Antarctic Summer
December, January, February

- Baby penguins are ready to be on their own.

- Adults spend their time hunting so they will have a thick layer of blubber for the winter.

- Adults come on shore to molt and grow new feathers.

27

★ strut

When you **strut**, you walk proudly with your head held high and your chest out.

The band leader *strutted* down the street at the front of the parade. What is another way to say "I walked proudly to the front of the class"?

un·set·tled

When someone is a little worried or nervous, he or she may feel **unsettled**.

When the puppy was in the house, the cat was *unsettled*. What makes you feel unsettled?

de·spite

Despite is another way to say "even though."

Anthony tripped and fell flat on his face. Anthony laughed at himself *despite* being embarrassed. What did Anthony do even though he was embarrassed?

★ = New

rec·og·nize

Recognize means to know who someone is.

We hadn't seen Miss Tam for several weeks, but we *recognized* her right away. How did we recognize Miss Tam?

Idioms and Expressions

★ keel o·ver

Keel over means to fall over.

The exhausted runner *keeled over* at the end of the race. What did the runner do? Why?

Now You Try It!

Try defining each word. Then look up the words in the glossary. Your definition might be better!

vast

Start with "A place that is *vast* is . . ."
Let's find the word on page 87.

con·ti·nent

Start with "A *continent* is . . ."
Let's find the word on page 82.

Thor, Emily, and the Little Successor

by Marilyn Sprick
illustrated by Neal Sharp

Chapter 1
It Happens to the Best

Across the vast Antarctic continent, summer
was almost over. In a few months, the land would
be wrapped in darkness. Blizzards would cross the
land. The Antarctic winter was about to begin. The
snow petrels, leopard seals, and humpback whales
were leaving for warmer places.

What were the animals doing for the winter?

A large emperor penguin named Thor watched
as the petrels took flight. "Humph," muttered Thor.

What do you think a petrel is? Why do you think Thor said, "Humph"?

Suddenly, a human appeared. Thor had heard about these two-legged creatures. He wasn't frightened. Still, without warning, Thor keeled over onto his back. Shocked at himself, Thor flipped onto his belly and was soon upright again.

"Humph," said Thor.

Describe what happened to Thor. Why do you think he said "Humph" again?

"Humph," said Emily with a giggle. "It happens to the best."

Without another word, Thor stood as tall as he could and strutted to the edge of the ice. He dove deep into the chilly ocean waters. Then he swam swiftly down through the icy dark waters.

On land, Emily chuckled.

Who are the main characters?

Down, down, 1,800 feet down in the ocean depths, Thor raced through the water. Speed! Power! Strength! At five years old, Thor was a ruler, an emperor of the sea.

After his shocking experience on land, Thor did not want to surface. He stayed underwater for 22 minutes. Thor thought, "I'll never leave the water again." Still, Thor felt unsettled. Something was odd, but Thor couldn't figure out what it was.

Emily and Thor's Questions

SETTING

Where does our story take place?

MAIN CHARACTER

Who are the two main characters?

CHARACTERIZATION

Why am I called an emperor of the sea?

PREDICTION

At the end of Chapter 1, Thor felt unsettled. Poor Thor. What do you think is going to happen to him?

Chapter 2
Are We There Yet?

The next day, Thor found himself on the solid ice again. He had been determined to swim, hunt, and eat in his icy ocean kingdom. Despite himself, Thor popped up out of the water onto the ice. A parade of older emperor penguins was on the move. Every March, Thor had watched the older penguins leap onto the ice and leave the sea.

This year, to his great surprise, Thor found himself marching with the others. Emily joined the parade as well. Thor looked at Emily and said, "Humph," but his feet kept moving.

"Humph," said Emily. Then she said again, "It happens to the best."

Thor said nothing as the winds blew across the ice. He wondered what he was doing. He missed zooming through the deep ocean water, but his feet kept moving—one mile, two miles, three miles. Thor could see nothing but white.

Another penguin fell into step with Thor. Thor recognized the other five-year-old, named Finn, but he didn't say anything. "Hey, Thor," squawked Finn. Thor was not in the mood to talk. Finn kept talking anyway. "Are we there yet?" asked Finn.

Thor shrugged and wondered, "Are we where?" Thor didn't say a word, but he knew that he had been here before.

Hours later, Finn squawked again, "Are we there yet?"

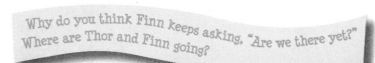

Why do you think Finn keeps asking, "Are we there yet?" Where are Thor and Finn going?

VOCABULARY POWER! 3

harsh

Something is **harsh** when it is uncomfortable, difficult, or rough.

The pioneers traveled through rain and snowstorms. The weather was . . .
What made the weather *harsh*?

★ trek

A **trek** is a difficult trip or journey.

The explorers left their boats and made the long and difficult journey to the South Pole. What did the explorers go on?

★ to·bog·gan

Toboggan means to slide across the snow.

Pam *tobogganed* down the hill on her sled. What did she do?

★ = New

★ in·stinct

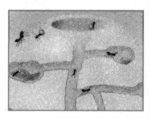

An **instinct** is something an animal does without being taught.

Ants build nests by *instinct*. They are born knowing how to build their nests. No one teaches them how.

Do you think reading is an instinct? Why or why not?

Idioms and Expressions

★ hun·ker down

When you **hunker down**, you get ready for something harsh.

A blizzard was coming, so the campers put on extra clothes and built a big fire. What did the campers do? Use your new expression.

Now You Try It!

Try defining the next word. Then look up the word in the glossary. Your definition might be better!

suc·ces·sor

Start with "A *successor* is . . ."
Let's find the word on page 86.

★ = New

Chapter 3
Almost There!

Thor did not like
to walk, but walk he did.
Ten miles, 11 miles, 12 miles,
15 miles, 20 miles, 40 miles.   The
winds grew even harsher, but the penguins
continued their trek. With each mile he walked,
Thor began to feel more and more determined.
Sometimes, he and the others tobogganed on their
stomachs—swooshing across the ice and snow.

What are the penguins doing? Describe their trek.

Finally, as they neared the end of their second day of walking and tobogganing, Thor recognized where he was. He was getting near the rookery where he was born. It was then that Thor answered Finn, "We are almost there."

When Thor and Finn arrived at the rookery, Emily, a penguin named Natalie, and the other females were waiting. Emily said to Thor, "I will lay an egg for us. Our baby will be our successor."

For humans, it was the worst of all weather on Earth. Winds raced across the ice at 120 miles per hour, and the temperature kept dropping—60 degrees below, 65 degrees below, 70 degrees below zero.

But for Emily and Thor and the hundreds of other penguins at the rookery, these were the finest of days. Each emperor female was laying an egg! And each emperor male would be a father. It was a time of great celebration.

What was it like at the rookery? Why was it a time of celebration? What do you think will happen next?

42

Emily laid a beautiful speckled egg. Emily and Thor were very proud! Then carefully, carefully, carefully, Emily passed the egg to Thor. Thor was a little surprised, but then instinct told him that Emily was right. As it had been for every generation of fathers before him, it would be his responsibility to take care of the egg. Thor was brave, strong, and very fat. He could go without food. But Emily was smaller. She would need to return to the sea to eat.

What is an instinct? What was Thor doing that every generation before him had done?

Emily and Thor sang together . . . a sad farewell song. "I will be back. I promise," said Emily. Then she, Natalie, and the other females began their parade back to the sea.

In the never-ending dark of the Antarctic winter, Thor and Finn huddled with the other male penguins in their colony. The fathers had their blubber and each other to keep them warm. Each penguin father had one precious egg on his feet.

Why do you think this might be a bittersweet time for the penguins? Why did the females leave?

One day, the ever-watchful Finn cried, "Oh, no!" At that, Thor looked out from the pack. An egg was rolling out across the ice. Unprotected, the penguin chick inside that egg would not survive—not even for a minute or two. Distressed, Finn said, "Oh, how sad."

Thor said nothing, but he checked on his egg. It was still carefully balanced on his feet. All was well. Finn checked on his egg. All was well. Their eggs were safe and warm. Thor and Finn hunkered down. These eggs would never leave their feet. Never!

Thor and Finn's Questions

ACTION

What do we penguin males do in winter? What do we do by instinct?

CAUSE AND EFFECT

What will happen to our eggs if we drop them on the ice? Do you think the moms will come back?

Chapter 4

The Little Successor

For 11 days, 12 days . . . 30 days, 40 days, 50 days . . . the penguin fathers waited. Very carefully, each penguin father moved slowly into the center of the huddle for warmth and then back out again. Finn loved the company. Even Thor took comfort in the community of penguin fathers. Each father would have his turn in the warm center.

How does the community help each penguin father?

Then one day, Finn cried, "It's moving!" Nearby, Thor also felt the chick in his egg move. With great pride Thor thought, "Ah, my successor is healthy and strong!"

Three days later, the eggs cracked open. A tiny, wet little chick sat on Thor's feet. Another tiny, wet little chick sat on Finn's feet. In the rookery, there were hundreds and thousands of successors. Thor had never known such a feeling of accomplishment. His chick was fine, and the rookery was a joyous place.

Why was the rookery a joyous place?

But where were the moms? On their way back . . . with bellies full! They were on their way back to the rookery to feed their chicks. Despite himself, Thor trumpeted and Emily heard. Finn trumpeted

and Natalie heard. The moms were close by. Soon Thor, Emily, and their little fluffy gray successor were together again. Finn, Natalie, and their little fluffy gray chick were happy to be a family. All over the rookery, families were meeting and greeting each other.

To his great surprise, Thor whooped and called out, "Life is good!"

Finn just smiled and thought, "Indeed, it is."

49

Thor bellowed, "I am an emperor, and this is . . . my successor!"

Emily smiled and quietly said, "It happens to the best."

The little penguin successor whistled and clicked.

Why did Thor bellow, "I am an emperor and this is my successor?" This story ended happily. How so?

Thor and Emily's Photo Album

Emily loves Thor

Our egg

Little successor

VOCABULARY POWER! 4

e·merge

Emerge means to come out of something.

Butterflies *emerge* from their chrysalises. What do butterflies do?

★ e·ter·nal

Eternal means forever. Something eternal will never end.

We hope the rain forest will be *eternal*. What does that mean?

★ tal·ons

Talons are sharp claws. Birds that hunt have talons.

The eagle's *talons* were two inches long. What are talons?

★ rare·ly

Rarely means hardly ever.

I *rarely* sleep in. How often do I sleep in? Use your new vocabulary word to tell me about something you don't do very often.

★ = New

★ ter·ri·to·ry

Some animals will claim a
piece of land as their own.
It is their **territory**.

My cat's *territory* is my backyard.
It doesn't want any other cats to
enter its . . .
What is my cat's territory?

The mountain lion's territory was the forest around the
lake. Where did the mountain lion live and hunt?

Now You Try It!

**Try defining the next words. Then look up the words in the
glossary. Your definition might be better!**

e·qua·tor

Start with "The *equator* is . . ."
Let's find the word on page 82.

pred·a·tor

Start with "A *predator* is . . ."
Let's find the word on page 84.

hes·i·tate

Start with "*Hesitate* means . . ."
Let's find the word on page 83.

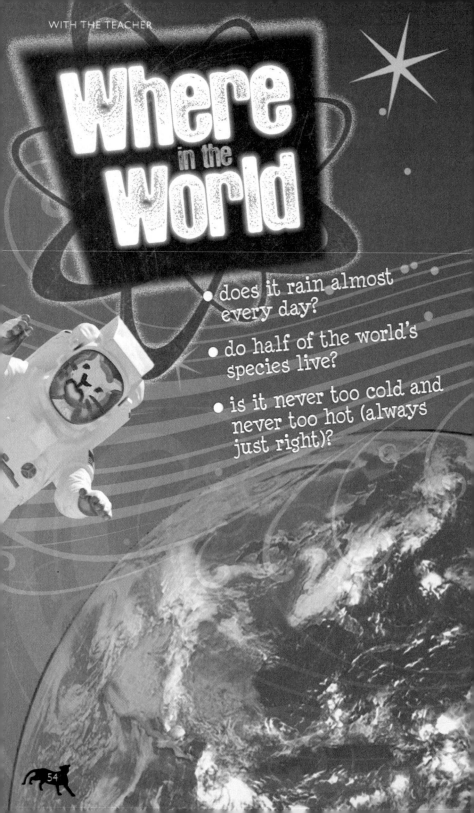

Where in the World

- does it rain almost every day?
- do half of the world's species live?
- is it never too cold and never too hot (always just right)?

Tropical Rain Forest

by Paula Rich

Answer:
The rain forests
of the world

Chapter 1

Layers of the Rain Forest

Wettest Places on Earth

Tropical rain forests are the wettest places on Earth. Rain forests get from 80 inches to 400 inches of rain each year. It may rain two inches in just one hour.

Tropical rain forests grow in the warmest parts of the Earth, around the equator. They are found on the continents of South America, North America, Africa, Asia, and Australia.

How are tropical rain forests different from Antarctica? Are there tropical rain forests near you?

FUN FACT

It is always warm and wet in a tropical rain forest. In fact, it rains almost every day of the year!

The Tropical Rain Forest

Emergent Layer

Tall trees tower above the forest, like umbrellas above a crowd of people. Some trees are more than 200 feet tall. They emerge from the forest.

Canopy

The rain forest canopy is formed by trees that grow from 70 to 100 feet tall. The leaves and branches grow together to form a thick layer.

Understory

The trees of the understory grow about 30 to 50 feet tall.

Forest Floor

There is little plant life on the forest floor, but lots of leaves, fruit, flowers, and animal waste fall from the canopy and understory to the forest floor.

This layer of treetops gets the most light and the most wind. It is not protected from the heavy rain. Birds and bats like to live in this layer.

The treetops of the canopy soak up most of the sunlight. Many plants and vines grow among the trees. Animals have many hiding places in the canopy. Monkeys, birds, snakes, and tree frogs live in this layer.

Below the canopy, the forest is dark, wet, and warm. Plants in the understory grow very slowly because there is so little sunlight. The flowers in this layer are brightly colored and have strong smells to attract insects, birds, and bats.

Little sunlight reaches the forest floor. It is warm, damp, and dark. Decomposers like earthworms recycle the waste to make soil for the trees. Big animals like deer, tapirs, and jaguars live on the forest floor.

Describe each layer of the rain forest. If you were an animal, which layer would you want to live in?

Children's Eternal Rain Forest of Costa Rica

Rain forests are a treasure to people all over the world, but many of the forests are being cut down. In 1987, a nine-year-old boy from Sweden decided he wanted to do something. But what?

Roland Tiensuu (Tee-en-soo) decided it would be a great idea to buy and protect a small piece of the rain forest. Roland's teacher and his class helped him earn money. Soon other children heard about Roland's idea. They all wanted to help. The children collected bottles and cans. They sold cookies. Some kids even asked for money for their birthdays so they could help buy some land in the rain forest.

All the money that the children earned and saved went to a group of people who lived in Costa Rica. They bought a little bit of the rain forest. This rain forest is called the Children's Eternal Rain Forest. It's eternal because it will never be cut down. It will be a rain forest forever!

At first, the Children's Eternal Rain Forest was only 15 acres. Children all over the world heard about it and sent money. The park grew and is still growing.

In 20 years, the Children's Eternal Rain Forest grew to cover 54,000 acres.

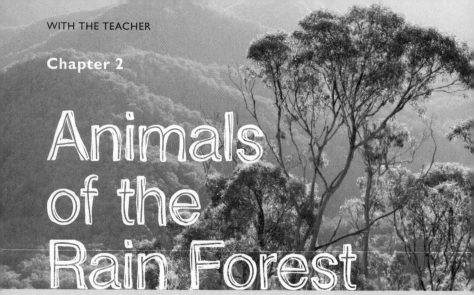

Chapter 2

Animals of the Rain Forest

Emergent Layer

Harpy Eagle

In the towering treetops of the rain forest, harpy eagles rule. These large carnivores are at the top of the rain forest food chain. They perch silently in the trees, watching and waiting for a good meal to pass by.

Harpies have excellent eyesight and hearing. They are agile flyers that can easily sail around the rain forest trees. When a hungry harpy eagle sees a monkey, sloth, or even a snake, it will swoop down and snatch the animal with its powerful feet. The harpy's talons can be the size of grizzly bear claws and just as sharp!

Harpy eagles may be three feet tall with a wingspan of nearly seven feet.

Harpy eagles nest in the tallest trees of the rain forests. They build their nests with large sticks and line them with soft leaves and feathers. The nests are huge—as large as your bed. Imagine sleeping in a bed of sticks perched in a tree 140 feet above ground!

Harpy eagles are rarely seen in the wild. Their rain forest habitat is being cut down for wood and farmland. Because these birds sometimes kill farm animals for food, farmers will often shoot any harpy eagle they see.

Describe a harpy eagle.
Why do you think harpy eagles might be endangered?

Canopy

Howler Monkey

Howler monkeys live in the trees of the rain forest canopy. They rarely visit the forest floor. Howler monkeys use their long strong tails as an extra arm while climbing and walking through the trees. These monkeys often hang from a branch by their tail, so they can use both hands for eating. They spend the day resting or searching for tasty leaves, fruits, and flowers to eat. At night, they sleep in the trees.

With a name like howler monkey, do you think these animals are quiet? No. Their deep, roaring howls can be heard three miles away! Groups of monkeys are called troops. Howler monkey troops howl every day at dawn and at dusk. Each troop is saying, "This is our territory! The food here belongs to us. Stay away!"

Mantled howler monkeys live in Costa Rica. They are between two and four feet tall and have short black fur with long golden hair along their sides.

Describe a howler monkey. What would an ordinary day be like in the life of a howler monkey?

Understory

Red-Eyed Tree Frog

In the shade of the understory, a toucan quietly creeps along a branch toward its prey. The toucan is looking very carefully for food. It almost misses the small bright green frog sleeping in the green leaves.

Suddenly, the sleeping frog senses the bird and

wakes, opening its huge eyes. The bright red eyes surprise the toucan. The toucan hesitates. In that split second, the frog uses its strong back legs to leap to safety. Blue and yellow stripes on the frog's legs flash as it jumps. The bird is confused by the quick movement and color. The frog is gone before the toucan knows what has happened.

The toucan has just missed having a red-eyed tree frog for lunch. These frogs have suction cups on their toes that help them hold onto tree branches. Red-eyed tree frogs are about two or three inches long. They live in the warm, moist environment of the rain forest understory. They eat insects at night and sleep during the day. As you learned, their big red eyes and colorful legs help protect them from predators.

Describe a red-eyed tree frog.

The red-eyed tree frog lives in the understory of the Costa Rican rain forest.

Forest Floor

Jaguar

In the darkness of the rain forest floor, a big spotted cat prowls. Eight feet long from its nose to the tip of its tail, a jaguar can weigh 250 pounds. They can have tan fur with black spots or black fur with black spots.

Jaguars live and hunt in the rain forests of Costa Rica.

These huge carnivores will eat almost any animal they can catch—snakes, monkeys, deer, turtles, or frogs. They spend most of their time on the forest floor, but sometimes they will climb a tree and pounce on their prey from above.

Unlike most cats, jaguars like the water. They swim, bathe, and play in streams and pools. They will even catch fish. Some people say a jaguar will use its long tail as fish bait. It waves its tail over the water or taps the water's surface with its tail. A hungry fish might think the jaguar's tail is food and come for a meal. Then the jaguar will quickly scoop up the fish with a big paw.

Scientists believe there may not be many jaguars left in the rain forests. It is hard to know how many jaguars there are because they are secretive animals. Jaguars usually live alone. They hunt mostly at night, so they are not often seen during the day.

Describe a jaguar. What makes a jaguar a successful predator?

★ con·serve

Conserve means to use less of something.

One way I *conserve* energy is to turn lights off. What's another way to save energy? Use your vocabulary word.

★ re·duce

Reduce means to use less of something.

To *reduce* our use of paper towels, we use cloth towels instead. How many paper towels do we use now?

re·cy·cle

Recycle means to use something again, usually after it has been made into something else. Used paper is recycled into new paper.

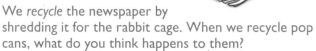

We *recycle* the newspaper by shredding it for the rabbit cage. When we recycle pop cans, what do you think happens to them?

★ re·use

Reuse means to use something again.

When you take the same homework folder home every day, you *reuse* the folder.

What else do you reuse? Use your new vocabulary word.

★ = New

★ com·post·ing

Composting is saving dead plants so they decay. The decayed plants can be mixed into soil to make the soil rich.

My mother likes *composting* because it's good for the environment. She puts potato peelings, lawn clippings, and coffee grounds into a pile near her garden. What is my mother doing?

Now You Try It!

Try defining the next words. Then look up the words in the glossary. Your definition might be better!

★ ex·cep·tion·al

Start with "Something is *exceptional* when . . ."
Let's find the word on page 83.

pro·tect

Start with "*Protect* means to . . ."
Let's find the word on page 84.

★ mar·vel·ous

Start with "*Marvelous* is another word for . . ."
Let's find the word on page 84.

Miss Tam's Corner

Now that you've read this issue of the *Science Digest*, you can understand why I think our home, the Earth we share, is . . .

amazing
awesome
dazzling
EXCEPTIONAL

fabulous

FANTASTIC

incredible

marvelous

SPLENDID

...perfect. Wouldn't you agree? Earth is so fine, I'm sure you would like to help protect our planet. Read on for tips on how to take care of Earth.

Why do you think Miss Tam thinks Earth is so wonderful?

Earth-Friendly Tips From Miss Tam

REDUCE, REUSE, RECYCLE
10 Things You Can Do to Help the Earth

REDUCE!

1 **Conserve energy.**
If you're not using it, turn it off. That means lights, televisions, computers, and video games—anything that uses electricity!

2 **Conserve paper.**
Try not to use paper towels and disposable cups and plates.

3 **Conserve water.**
Use only what you need. Keep your showers short and don't let the water run while you brush your teeth.

Name three ways you can help take care of Earth by reducing what you use.

Poster contributed by
Ana Lopez, the Bronx, New York

Every Day Is Earth Day
by Ana
Lopez

Reduce Litter!
Keep our Earth Exceptional!

Look at the poster. What do you think Ana's class is studying?

REUSE!

4 Write on both sides of the paper.

5 Reuse folders and notebooks.

6 Take your lunch to school in a reusable bag or plastic container.

7 Bring your own bag or backpack to the grocery store instead of using a plastic or paper bag.

Name three ways you can help take care of Earth by reusing what you use.

Poster contributed
by Ben Wright,
the Bronx, New York

RECYCLE!

8 Set up recycle bins at home. Make it a habit to recycle newspapers, cans, plastic, and glass.

9 Make your own wrapping paper using old calendar pictures or old drawings.

10 Create a composting bin with your parents' help. Food scraps can go in the bin instead of into the trash. The scraps will turn into rich soil for the garden.

Name three ways you can help take care of Earth by recycling what you use.

Poster contributed
by Maya Martinez,
the Bronx, New York

Magnificent and Marvelous
Earth and Me
by Maya Martinez

It's Not Yucky! It's Just Ducky!

Reduce Waste by Composting!

Miss Tam's Note to You

Dear Readers:

Oh my. It's time to say goodbye already. My work as guest editor for this *Read Well Science Digest* has come to an end. I hope you enjoyed reading about the wonders of the Earth we share.

It has been an eventful year for me. I've traveled to Ghana, Hawaii, the Great Barrier Reef, Antarctica, and Costa Rica. Minnie Bird and Scraggly Cat are happy to have me home for a while. We are planning my next adventures, though. Can you guess where?

Sampai jumpa (sump-ay joomp-a),
Ciao (chou),
Adiós (ah-dee-os),
Miss Tam, Scraggly Cat, and Minnie Bird

Glossary

Antarctic

The **Antarctic** is the land at the bottom of the Earth.

The *Antarctic* is another name for the continent of Antarctica.

Arctic

The **Arctic** is the area at the top of the Earth.

The *Arctic* is a very cold area.

blizzard

When it is snowing and the wind is blowing hard, it is called a **blizzard**.

The news report said schools were closed because of the *blizzard*.

composting

Composting is saving dead plants so they decay. The decayed plants can be mixed into soil to make the soil rich.

My mother likes *composting* because it's good for the environment. She puts potato peelings, lawn clippings, and coffee grounds into a pile near her garden. What is my mother doing?

conserve

Conserve means to use less of something.

One way I *conserve* energy is to turn lights off.

Glossary

continent

A **continent** is one of seven large land areas on Earth.

The United States is on the *continent* of North America.

despite

Despite is another way to say "even though."

Anthony laughed at himself *despite* being embarrassed.

emerge

Emerge means to come out of something.

Butterflies *emerge* from their cocoons.

equator

If you drew a line around the middle of the Earth, that would be the **equator**.

If you stand at the *equator*, it is the same distance to the top of the Earth and the bottom of the Earth.

eternal

Eternal means forever. Something eternal will never end.

Some people believe that the universe is *eternal*.

exceptional

Something is **exceptional** when it is so good there is nothing else like it.

Elsa did an *exceptional* job on her science project.

freezing

When it is so cold that water turns to ice, it is called **freezing**.

We looked outside and saw that the pond had turned to ice, so we knew it was *freezing*.

harsh

Something is **harsh** when it is uncomfortable, difficult, or rough.

The pioneers traveled through rain, snowstorms, and other *harsh* weather.

hesitate

Hesitate means to stop before saying or doing something. You hesitate because you aren't sure what to do.

When a cat ran by, the dog *hesitated* and then ran after the cat.

Glossary

instinct

An **instinct** is something an animal does without being taught.

Ants build nests by *instinct*.

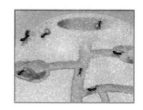

marvelous

Marvelous is another word for wonderful and fantastic.

We had a *marvelous* time at the park.

predator

A **predator** is an animal that hunts other animals for food.

A spider is a *predator* because it traps and eats insects.

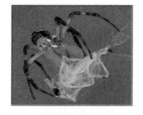

protect

Protect means to keep safe.

Mother gorillas *protect* their babies.

rarely

Rarely means hardly ever.

I *rarely* sleep in.

recognize

Recognize means to know who someone is.

We hadn't seen Miss Tam for several weeks, but we *recognized* her right away.

recycle

Recycle means to use something again, usually after it has been made into something else. Used paper is recycled into new paper.

We *recycle* the newspaper by shredding it for the rabbit cage.

reduce

Reduce means to use less of something.

To *reduce* our use of paper towels, we use cloth towels instead.

reuse

Reuse means to use something again.

When you take the same homework folder home every day, you *reuse* the folder.

strut

When you **strut**, you walk proudly with your head held high and your chest out.

The band leader *strutted* down the street at the front of the parade.

Glossary

successor

A **successor** is the person who takes over someone's job.

Bill retired as the coach of the baseball team. The new coach is Grace. Grace is Bill's *successor*.

talons

Talons are sharp claws. Birds that hunt have talons.

The eagle's *talons* were two inches long.

temperature

The **temperature** tells us how hot or cold something is.

The weather report says the *temperature* outside is 59 degrees.

territory

Some animals will claim a piece of land as their own. It is their **territory**.

Where an eagle hunts is called its *territory*.

toboggan

Toboggan means to slide across the snow.

Pam *tobogganed* down the icy hill on her sled.

trek

A **trek** is a difficult trip or journey.

The explorers left their boats and made the long *trek* to the South Pole.

unique

Unique means very special or one of a kind.

Each person has *unique* fingerprints.

unsettled

When someone is a little worried or nervous, he or she may feel **unsettled**.

When the puppy was in the house, the cat was *unsettled*. What makes you feel unsettled?

vast

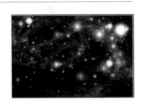

A place that is **vast** is very great in size. It is enormous.

Space is *vast*.

Glossary

hunker down

When you **hunker down**, you get ready for something harsh.

A blizzard was coming, so the campers put on extra clothes and *hunkered down* around a big fire.

keel over

Keel over means to fall over.

The exhausted runner *keeled over* at the end of the race.